King Kevin

Paul Blum

Editorial consultants:
Cliff Moon and Lorraine Petersen

RISING★STARS

nasen
NASEN House, 4/5 Amber Business Village, Amber Close,
Amington, Tamworth, Staffordshire B77 4RP

Rising Stars UK Ltd.
22 Grafton Street, London W1S 4EX
www.risingstars-uk.com

Text, design and layout © Rising Stars UK Ltd.
The right of Paul Blum to be identified as the author of
this work has been asserted by him in accordance with the
Copyright, Design and Patents Act 1988.

Published 2007

Cover design: Button plc
Illustrator: Chris King
Text design and typesetting: Andy Wilson
Publisher: Gill Budgell
Commissioning editor: Catherine Baker
Publishing manager: Lesley Densham
Editor: Clare Robertson
Editorial consultants: Cliff Moon and Lorraine Petersen

British Library Cataloguing in Publication Data.
A CIP record for this book is available from the British Library

ISBN: 978-1-84680-207-2

Printed by Craft Print International Limited, Singapore

Contents

Characters

Alfie Alfie is starting at a new school.
He is in Year 10.

Spiro Alfie's friend at his
new school.

Tyrone Leader of a Year 10 gang.
He wants to take over from King Kevin.

Sal One of Tyrone's gang.

King Kevin Kevin is in Year 11.
He is called 'King' because
he rules the school.

The Narrator The Narrator
tells the story.

Scene 1

New boy

Narrator	Alfie is in Year 10. He is new to the school. Spiro is showing him around on his first day. They are in the queue for lunch when Tyrone, his friend Sal and their gang push in.
Alfie	Don't we all have to queue?
Tyrone	Doesn't look like it, does it?
Spiro	Let's come back later.
Tyrone	Stay where you are. I don't want you grassing me up.

Narrator Tyrone grabs Spiro and
pushes him against the wall.

Spiro Leave me alone.

Sal Look at his skinny little arms.
He's like a Year 7.

Tyrone Yeah!

Alfie Why don't you leave him alone?

Tyrone Are you talking to me?

Alfie I said, leave him alone.

Tyrone What's it got to do with you?

Alfie He hasn't done anything to you.

Tyrone Are you trying to start something?

Narrator Tyrone pushes Alfie, again and again.
A crowd gathers around.
They think there will be a fight.

Sal This new boy is a dead man walking.

Tyrone   Look at his clothes.
             They're from a charity shop.

Alfie   They're new!

Spiro   Leave it, Alfie.
             Don't argue.
             Just come with me.

Narrator Alfie and Spiro go outside.

Alfie   I've made a bad start at this school.
             Nobody likes me.

Spiro   They don't like me either and
             I've been around ages.

Alfie   Why's that?

Spiro   I don't have the right type of trainers.
I do my homework.
They say I creep to the teachers.

Alfie   So do they treat you bad all the time?

Spiro   Yeah.

Alfie   Why do you put up with it?

Spiro   What choice have I got?
Anyway, let's get to lessons.
We've got maths next but
I've got to go to the loo first.
You go ahead – it's down there.

Narrator   Alfie goes one way
and Spiro goes the other.
Suddenly, three kids come towards
Alfie with scarves over their faces.

Tyrone   Empty your pockets.

Alfie   My new iPod!

Sal   Shut your mouth, you fool.

Alfie   Give it back.

Tyrone   Ssshh, or I'll slap you.

Alfie   My dinner money!

Tyrone   I'll remember your face.
So make sure you fill up your wallet
for me tomorrow.

Narrator The robbers laugh and walk off.
Spiro hears the noise and comes
back to see what has happened.

Spiro Are you okay?

Alfie Yeah – I guess. Three kids just came
and nicked my iPod and money.
I'm sure one of them was Tyrone.

Spiro I can lend you some dinner money.

Alfie Thanks, mate. But someone's
got to stop that Tyrone.

Spiro It's no good trying to get
back at him. The only way
is to keep your head down.

Alfie I just think he's got it coming
to him … somehow.

Narrator Later, Tyrone and his gang
are checking out the stolen goods
in the toilets.

Scene 1   New boy

Tyrone   I don't like King Kev. He's stuck up.

Sal   You don't like him
because he blanks you.

Tyrone   Leave it out.

Sal   But if he said 'Jump',
you'd say 'How high?'

Tyrone   No way. He's getting old and lazy.

Sal   So who's the new king in this school?

Tyrone   You're looking at him.

Scene 2
Meeting the King

Narrator	In Jim's café after school, pupils wait to buy sweets and drinks. King Kevin's gang are the top gang in the school. They sit at their own table.
Alfie	Who's that?
Spiro	The King and his gang. That's Kevin – King Kevin.
Alfie	King?

Spiro   He runs the school.
Kids have more respect for him
than the headteacher.

Alfie   Yeah?

Spiro   You bet. If he doesn't like a teacher,
then they don't have a lesson.

Alfie   What do you mean?

Spiro   The pupils muck about
or just bunk off.

Alfie   Right.

Spiro   Oh no – there's Tyrone.
I'm out of here.

Alfie   Okay – I'll just finish this and
then I'm off too.

Spiro   See you later, mate.

Alfie   Yeah.

Narrator Tyrone goes up to the King.
He is trying to look important,
but he just looks scared.

Tyrone I want to do some business.

Kevin What kind of business?

Narrator Tyrone passes over the iPod
that he stole from Alfie.

Kevin I don't want that.
Where did you get it?

Tyrone   Out there.

Kevin   You took it off a new kid,
didn't you?

Tyrone   So what?

Kevin   So the teachers are blaming us.
They're blaming my gang.

Tyrone   Business is business.
Nobody saw us.

Kevin   Somebody did.

Tyrone   Who cares about them?

Kevin   I do. Sit down here.

Narrator   Tyrone is scared
but he tries to hide it.

Kevin   You've been meddling
in my business.
Showing off.

Tyrone   You what?

Kevin   I've got this school sorted.
No hassles.
I don't want you messing it up.
Understand?

Narrator   Tyrone says nothing.

Kevin   In a gang, are you?

Tyrone   Yeah.

Narrator   The King takes hold of Tyrone's shirt.
He pushes him up against the wall.

Kevin   I don't like your tone.
Show some respect.

Narrator   King Kevin lets go of Tyrone.
Tyrone runs out, shaking with anger.
The rest of his gang follow him
outside. They don't notice Alfie
leaving the café.
Alfie hears everything they say.

Tyrone   Nobody treats me like that.

Sal   Somebody just did.

Tyrone   Who does he think he's messing with?

Sal   But who told on us?

Tyrone   We'll find that out soon enough.
Then it's time for King Kevin
to get a lesson he won't forget.

Sal   What sort of lesson?

Tyrone   A lesson that will wipe
the silly smile off his face.
We'll hit him when it's easy –
on his way to school.

Sal   Good idea.

Tyrone   We'll steam him from behind.
Destroy him.

Scene 3

Danger!

Narrator Alfie slips back into the café.
He has heard everything.
He knows he has to warn Kevin
that he is in danger.
He goes up to King Kevin's table.

Kevin Let him through.

Alfie Thanks.

Kevin You're welcome.
So who are you?

Alfie Alfie Stone. 10T.

Kevin Where do you live, Alfie?

Alfie   On the South Town Estate.

Kevin   Same roots as me.
          So what can we do for you?

Alfie   I've got to tell you something.

Kevin   Come on then, spit it out.

Alfie   I can only tell you.

Kevin   A secret, eh?

Alfie   Kind of.

Kevin   Okay then – come outside.
          You can tell me there.

Narrator   King Kevin and Alfie go outside.

Kevin   So what's to tell?

Alfie   Hang on – I just need to check
no one can hear.

Kevin   Come on – get on with it.
This better be important!

Alfie   Tyrone in Year 10 is planning
to beat you up.

Kevin   Who is Tyrone?

Alfie   In the café just now –
trying to sell the iPod.

Kevin   That little loser.
And he reckons he can
beat me up, does he?

Alfie   He's a good fighter.
I should know.

Kevin   How come?

Alfie   That iPod – he stole it off me.

Kevin   Ha! I should've got it off him.
Then you could've had it back
for tipping me off!

Alfie   Listen, they're going to wait for you
on the way to school tomorrow.

Kevin   Right. Well maybe I'll be waiting
for them … I owe you one.

Alfie   That's okay.

Narrator The next morning, Tyrone's gang wait at the corner of the block of flats where King Kevin lives.

Tyrone Where is he?

Sal I'm bored. It's freezing out here.

Tyrone He's got to come out soon.

Sal If he doesn't turn up in the next ten minutes, I'm off.

Tyrone No one leaves here until I say so.

Sal Oh yeah?

Tyrone Yeah.

Narrator But nobody comes out of the flats.

Sal Come on, we'll be late for school.

Tyrone Since when did you care about being late for school?

Sal But I'm freezing!

Tyrone Okay. You win. Let's go.

Sal I reckon someone must have tipped King Kev off.

Tyrone Yeah – and I reckon I know who it was …

Narrator Soon after, Alfie is sitting
in an English lesson.
He is worried because
Spiro's seat is empty.
He finds a note in his bag.
He reads it.

Alfie Alfie, Tyrone is after me.
He has found out what we know.
I have gone to hide at the back
of the school. I will stay here
until the end of school.
Come and find me
as soon as you can. Spiro.

Narrator As soon as the lesson ends,
Alfie runs out of the classroom
and down to the back
of the school.

Alfie Spiro! Spiro! Are you there?

Narrator Alfie hears a noise behind a bush.
It is the sound of somebody crying.

Spiro Alfie. They made me write that note
to get you to come here. I'm sorry!

Narrator Alfie sees that Spiro has been tied up.
He hears a voice behind him.

Tyrone You grassed us.

Alfie I did what?

Spiro He didn't understand.
He was new in the school.

Tyrone Shut your mouth, baby boy.

Narrator Tyrone pushes Alfie down.
He rubs his face in the mud.

Alfie Get off me.

Tyrone You'll wish you had never
come to this school.
You'll wish you had never been born
by the time I'm finished with you.

Spiro No!

Scene 4
King Alfie?

Narrator It is the beginning of afternoon school. The corridors are jam packed with kids going to lessons. But King Kevin and his gang are going the other way.

Kevin Come on, we've got a job to do.

Narrator About 50 kids run after Kevin and his gang. They all go down to the bushes behind school. The headteacher notices something is going on. He follows them.

Kevin So it's you again, Tyrone.

Sal Look who it is, Tyrone!

Tyrone   Lazy fat cat Kev.
          What are you doing down here?

Kevin   There's a friend who needs our help.

Tyrone   A friend? Yeah, right!

Spiro   You don't know what a friend is,
          Tyrone.

Tyrone   Shut up, you.

Kevin   Just leave the kid alone.

Narrator Tyrone is still sitting on Alfie's back,
pushing his face in the mud.
Alfie is trying to get up.

Kevin I said, leave the kid alone.

Tyrone You're history, King Kevin.
I'm in charge now.

Narrator Kevin begins to smile and
walks towards Tyrone.

Tyrone King, King, King.
Come on, King Kev!

Sal Yeah, come on.
Let's see what you're made of!

Narrator Tyrone jumps up and lands a punch
on Kevin. King Kevin is too slow
and the punch lands hard.
He bends over in pain.
Alfie gets up and steps forward.

Tyrone   You keep out of this.

Alfie   Kevin?

Kevin   Do as he says.
It's between him and me.

Tyrone   Come on King Kevin – your
royal highness. Fight me.

Narrator   Tyrone punches Kevin in the face.
The King moans in pain.
He holds his head in his hands.
The crowd of kids cannot believe it.

Alfie   You've got to stop this.

Spiro   Be careful, Alfie!

Tyrone   Don't worry, you're next, you wimp.

Sal   Yeah, I'll thump him for you, Tyrone!

Narrator King Kevin is sitting on the ground.
Tyrone starts to kick him
but suddenly he trips.
The King has got up and
is holding Tyrone round the knees.
Kevin gets Tyrone in a bear hug.

Tyrone Get off me, you nutter.
You're going to break my neck!

Kevin Perhaps I should.
What do you reckon, Alfie?

Narrator For a moment, the crowd is silent.
Even the headteacher says nothing.

Alfie I think you should let him go.

Tyrone Help me. Somebody help me.
He's going to kill me!

Kevin   No, I'm not, it's your lucky day.
Get back to your lessons, folks.
The show is over.

Narrator   The headteacher comes to the front
of the crowd. Kevin drops Tyrone in
front of the headteacher and leaves.
The crowd of kids do as they are told
and go back to lessons.

Spiro   That was really brave, Alfie.

Alfie   Yeah – or really stupid.
They'll both be after me now.

Narrator   After school that day,
Jim's café is very busy.
Everybody is talking about
what happened between
Tyrone and Kevin. King Kevin sees
Alfie and Spiro coming in.
He waves them over.

Spiro   Look out – King Kevin's seen us.
Let's get out of here.

Alfie   No, hang on. I'm not scared of Kevin.

Spiro   Okay then, but keep your head down.

Kevin   Come and join us.

Spiro   No way! He wants us
to sit at his table!

Kevin   Got a few minutes, lads?

Alfie   Of course we have.

Kevin   Drinks – anything you fancy –
it's on me.

Spiro   Black coffee please.

Alfie   And me.

Kevin   So, are you two feeling better?

Spiro   We're fine.

Kevin   Squeeze up guys, let my two
new friends sit here with us.

Narrator Kevin's gang move up.
The whole café are looking
at Spiro and Alfie.

Kevin I'd have pulped Tyrone for you if you'd
asked me to. Why didn't you?

Alfie It just all seemed a bit stupid – you
thumping him, him thumping you.
What's it all for?

Kevin You've got to keep people like Tyrone
in their place, haven't you?
Or else other folks can't go about
their business in peace.
Get themselves an education.

Alfie Yeah, I guess.
It's just not my kind of thing.

Kevin   That's a shame.
Cos I've been thinking – there's
a place for you in my gang,
if you want it.

Spiro   In your gang?

Kevin   Yeah – you too, if you want.

Alfie   Thanks. But I don't think
that would work.

Kevin   Why not? I'm leaving school
at the end of the term.
You could even make it to be
King Alfie. How about that?

Spiro   King Alfie!

Alfie   Thanks a lot, Kevin.
But I don't want to be king.

Narrator   Alfie gets up from the table.
King Kevin stands up
and shakes his hand.
Kevin watches Alfie go.
As Alfie walks across the café,
all the other kids stand up too.

Spiro   I think he's going to be King Alfie,
even if he doesn't want to.
Just a different sort of king.

Drama ideas

After Scene 1

- Hotseating: choose one person to take the role of Tyrone.
- The others can ask Tyrone questions to find out why he bullies other kids, and why he wants to be 'the new king' in school.

After Scene 2

- What do you think will happen next? Talk about this for two minutes in your group.
- Decide on an idea between you, e.g. maybe Alfie will tell King Kevin, or try to stop Tyrone.
- Act out your idea in your group.

After Scene 3

- How are Alfie and Spiro going to get away from Tyrone's gang?
- In your group, act out what might happen next.

After Scene 4

- Choose a character from the play.
- What do you think they did next, after the end of the play? Talk about this in pairs.
- Then take turns to tell the rest of the group what your character did next.